We Go Exploring

Jens Kargaard and Minna Ekberg

Photographs by
Otto Wikkelsø
Jens Kargaard

A LION BOOK

Copyright © 1984 Forlaget Scandinavia, Copenhagen, Denmark

Published by
Lion Publishing plc
Icknield Way, Tring, Herts, England
ISBN 0 85648 703 1
Albatross Books
PO Box 320, Sutherland, NSW 2232, Australia
ISBN 0 86760 478 6

First edition 1984

English text by Meryl Doney

Printed in Singapore

'What do worms do all day?'
'How does a caterpillar become a butterfly?'
'How can you tell the age of a tree?'

These are just some of the questions
Mark and Emma consider on their day out
in the country with Uncle George.

There are so many exciting things to see
– and lots of surprises too.
And Uncle George shows the children
what to look for, as well as how to
look after and enjoy the world around them.

Mark and Emma didn't want to waste a single
minute. As soon as the birds woke them, they got
dressed and ran out into the field to see the cows.
    They were staying with Uncle George in the
country. Mum and Dad had brought them down to
Uncle George's house the night before. Now they
had the whole day to spend with him.

Uncle George was a Warden in the national park.
He helped to look after the forest and the animals
that lived there.

Over breakfast they talked about what to do.

'I have some work to do in my garden this morning,'
said Uncle George. 'So you children can play outside.
Then we can take a picnic and go exploring in the forest.
You never know, we may even see some wild deer.'

They went out into the garden. There were flowers
of every shade and colour. Emma watched the bee
collecting nectar to make honey. She looked round
the garden.

    'Isn't it lovely,' she said.

    'And God made it all,' said Uncle George.
'He has certainly made a wonderful world for us to
live in. There are surprises wherever you look.'

'See this little caterpillar,' he said, pointing
to a wiggly green creature crawling on a cabbage
leaf. 'A few weeks ago that was a tiny yellow
egg. Soon it will build itself into a hard green
cocoon. Then out will come – a butterfly!'

Uncle George began to hoe the ground.
'Here's another special creature,' he said,
bending down to pick something up. He put it gently
onto Mark's open hand.
'Ugh!' cried Mark. 'It's a worm.'

'Now, he's really useful,' laughed Uncle George.
'He digs his way through the earth, making it
soft and good for my vegetables to grow in.'

'It tickles!' squeaked Mark.

'That's because he's not used to the sunlight
or your hot hand,' laughed Uncle George. 'Let's put
him back now, so that he can get on with his work.'

'Look,' Emma said suddenly. 'The blackbird's got
a worm.'

'He certainly has to work hard to get his lunch,'
said Uncle George, laughing. 'But if birds didn't
eat worms, there would be too many of them
in the garden.'

Emma wandered off to look at the flowers. The garden was full of pink roses.

'Uncle George,' she called, 'flowers don't lay eggs like the butterfly and they can't move about. How do they have babies?'

'Ah, but they do have eggs,' explained Uncle George, looking up from his hoeing. 'We call them seeds. Every plant has seeds. And because they can't move about, they have some marvellous ways of spreading them. Take one of those dandelions, Emma, and give it a good blow.'

Emma took a deep breath and puffed. All the fluffy
bits came off. As they floated away, she could
see a tiny seed under each one.

'Parachutes!' said Mark. 'They've got parachutes.'

'Yes,' said Uncle George. 'Each one will take
its seed to a new place where it can grow.'

'And look at your socks, Mark!' chuckled Uncle George. 'That's another way seeds travel. They hitch a ride by getting stuck onto animals' fur. And even boys' socks!'

The children spent the rest of the morning
playing in the garden. Then Uncle George
finished his work, packed up their picnic and
they set out for the woods.

The first thing they found was a baby bird.
It had fallen out of the nest.

'We should leave it for the mother bird to
find,' said Emma.

'I know all about birds,' Emma said. 'We've been doing it at school. Our teacher showed us a real nest, and lots of pictures of eggs and baby birds.'

'Be very quiet,' whispered Uncle George. He pointed up into a tree. There was a nest with a mother bird and her babies.

'She's a good mother, isn't she?' said Emma.

'Yes,' said Uncle George. 'She reminds me of God. He cares for us, just like the mother bird.'

'In fact,' said Uncle, looking up at the sky,
'we can learn a lot about God from the things he
has made.'

They all watched as a hawk hovered overhead.

'We've learned to fly in aeroplanes by
watching the birds,' he said.

'It's quite incredible what birds can do. Many
of them fly thousands of miles to warmer countries
every winter. When I see them all together, flying
into the sunset, I think how great God is to make
them all.'

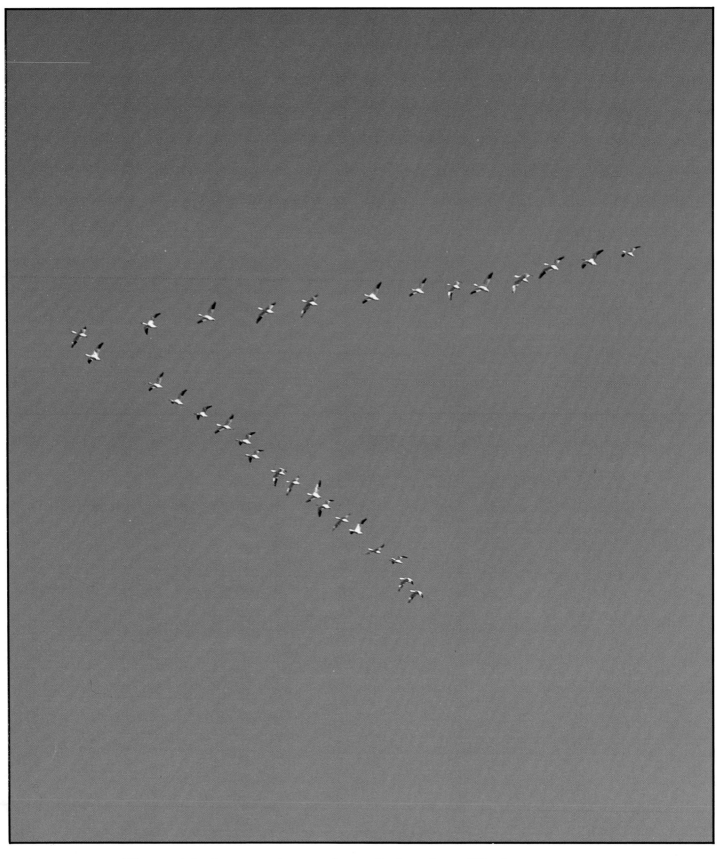

'Some birds travel together, flying in a V-shape with one bird leading the way.'

'How does *he* know the way?' asked Mark.

'I'm afraid that's something we don't know yet,' replied Uncle George.

'Look,' he said, pointing towards the
farmhouse. 'Our friendly martin flies half-way
round the world every year. But he always finds
his way back to his own nest under our roof.'

'It's one of God's surprises!' laughed Emma.

She jumped up and began to run along a tree trunk.

'I'm a martin, flying round the world. Come on, follow me.'

'Do you know how to tell the age of a tree?' asked Uncle George, catching them up.

'By their birthdays?' asked Emma.

By now it was lunchtime. They found a spot by
the river to eat their picnic. The children
decided to pick some flowers. They were careful
not to pull up the roots.

'How many flowers do you think there are in
that field?' called Uncle George.

'One, two, three...a thousand...a trillion!'
counted Mark.

 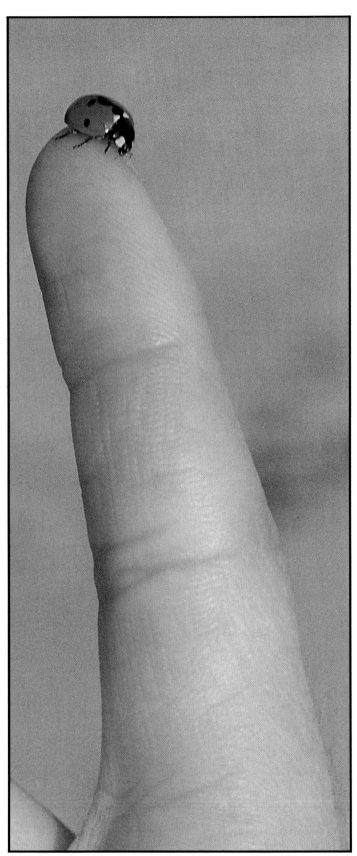

'God's not just interested in the big, old
things like trees. He can make tiny things too
– like these,' said Uncle George, pointing to a
little group of ladybirds.

'Oh, I love ladybirds,' said Emma, taking one
onto her finger and watching it till it flew away.

After lunch the children wanted to play.
    'We'll hide and you find us,' they
called as they ran off.
    Uncle George began to count. 'One, two,
three, four. . .'

Uncle George was good at finding them. He knew every part of the woods. Suddenly he called out, 'Come and look at this, children.'

He held up a broken bottle and a plastic wrapper.

'It makes me very angry and sad to find things like this left lying about.'

So they changed their game to 'hunt the rubbish',
and Mark and Emma collected a big pile of litter
for Uncle George to take away later.

They didn't want the animals to get hurt
by stepping on broken glass, or by eating
the plastic wrapper.

It was fun hiding behind the big trees
in the forest.

'Dumping rubbish like that is just the opposite
of what God wants us to do in his world,'
said Uncle George as they walked on. 'He wants
us to look after the world.'
    'How can we do that?' asked Emma.

'By looking after the land and taking care of the creatures,' replied Uncle George. 'For instance, I always keep some hay for the wild deer in winter, in case they can't find any food.'

'Uncle,' said Mark thoughtfully, 'I don't like everything God has made. I hate snakes and toads and cold slithery things.'

'Oh, I love them,' said Emma. 'It's insects and buzzy creatures I don't like!'

'Well now,' said Uncle George. 'It's not really
a matter of what we like and don't like. God has
made each one with its own special work to do.
The snakes and toads eat flies and bugs, so they're
very useful.'

Just then they came to a bridge over a stream.
The three of them stopped to look down at the
cool water.

They went down to the water's edge.
    'Just think,' said Uncle George, 'of all the little creatures living here in the stream. Some of them are so small that you can hardly see them.'
    'Look at that tiny fish,' said Emma.

Then Mark and Emma lay down on their tummies
to look at all the tiny creatures running about
on the ground. They saw some ants. 'They look
so busy,' said Emma.

'Did you know that they live in tiny cities,
as well-run as any of ours?' asked Uncle George.
'Each ant does his own work and that helps
all the rest.'

Further downstream they found some ducks and
moorhens. The children watched them enjoying
the water.

'Look!' squealed Emma, 'I've found a baby
frog. I'll put it down your neck, Mark!'

Mark leaped out of the way.
   'I'll put a spider down yours!' he shouted
back and they all laughed.

'Come on,' said Uncle George. 'We'd better put
the poor frog back by the stream before he dies
of fright.'

The sun was setting as they walked home. It was Uncle George's turn to look thoughtful.

'Even though it's God's world,' he said, 'it's not exactly the way he wants it to be. It can be a cruel place because we've spoilt it. One day he will put it right again and then it will be a wonderful place.'

Suddenly he stopped and pointed.

'Look, over there,' he whispered.

Far ahead, standing at the edge of the trees, stood two deer. They all held their breath as the gentle creatures looked about them and sniffed the air. Then, as quietly as they had come, the deer turned and disappeared into the woods.

After supper that evening, Uncle George read to
them from the first book of the Bible, Genesis:
    'So God created human beings. . . He said, "Have
many children, so that your descendants will live
all over the earth and bring it under their control.
I am putting you in charge of the fish, the birds,
and all the wild animals."'

'You see,' said Uncle George, 'God put us here to look after his world – and to enjoy it.'

'I did enjoy today, it was smashing,' said Mark sleepily. 'We saw so much. The worm and the baby bird, the old tree and the tiny frog...'

'And we did see the wild deer,' said Emma.
'They made it really special.'

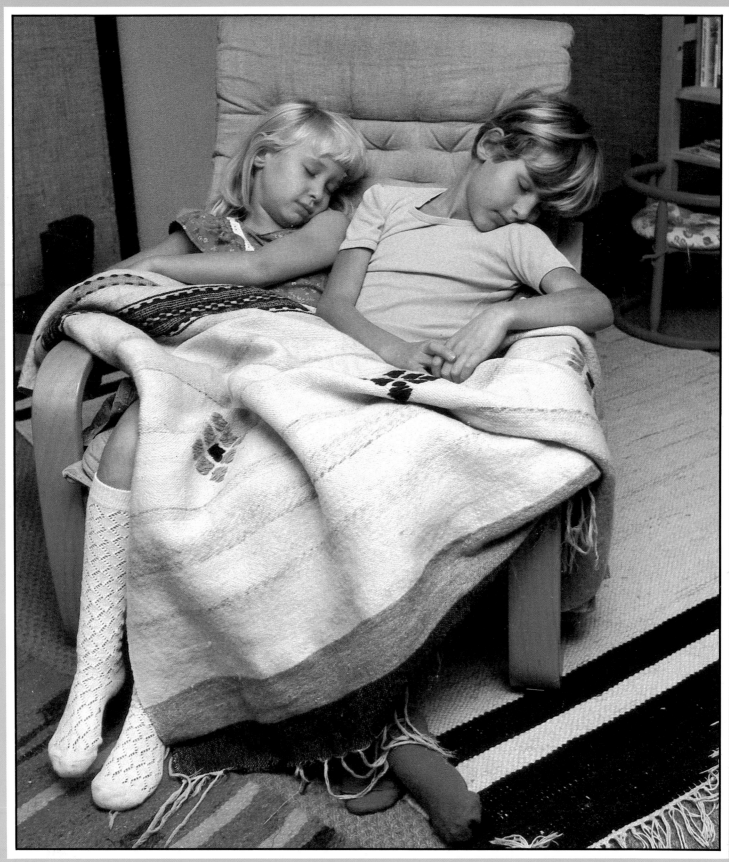

Mark and Emma had spent such an exciting day out in the fresh country air, that when Mum and Dad came to pick them up later that evening, they found them both fast asleep in Uncle George's big armchair.